This book belongs to :
Dieses Heft gehört:

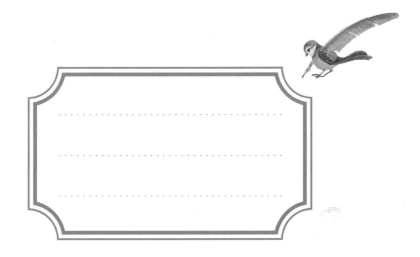

: . . . .

: . . . .

: . . . .

✿ *Brause*

My first steps..
Meine ersten Schritte mit der Feder

TOOLS NEEDED

- a nib holder
- a pointed nib for Copperplate lettering
- a broad-edged nib for Italic lettering
- an ink bottle

NOTWENDIGES MATERIAL

- ein Federhalter
- eine Feder für die Englische Schreibschrift
- Eine besondere Feder für die runde Schrift
- ein Tintenfläschen

PREPARING A NIB FOR CALLIGRAPHY

New nibs come lightly covered whith grease or varnish for protection, They must be cleaned before the first use.

Wash the nib in soapy water. Dry the nib and dip it in ink. Write a few letters and dry the nib again. The nib is now ready for lettering.

VORBEREITUNG EINER KALLIGRAPHIEFEDER.

Neue Federn sind häufig noch mit einer Fett- oder Ölschicht benetz, es ist also notwending die Federn vor der ersten Verwendung zu reinigen.

Reinige die Feder mit etwas Seifenlauge. Wische die Feder ab und tauche sie zum ersten Male in Tinte. Schreibe zwei oder drei Worte und trockne die Feder anschließend noch einmal ab. Deine Feder ist nun schreibfertig.

When lettering Copperplate,
use one of the following
Brause nibs.

Um diese Schrift zu realisieren,
empfehlen wir
folgende Schreibfedern.

School/die Zeichenfeder

Steno/die Stenofeder

Steel Script/die Pfannenfeder

Gold Script/die Schreibfeder Cito Fein

Small Steno/die Fingerfeder

After the Renaissance, the writing of official documents cha
 Ascender (upper portion of the letter),
and descender
(lower portion of the letter) become slante
Lettering is changing with the invention
of pointed nibs made of flexible metal.
They will replace nibs made from bird feathers,
the original tool for Copperplate lettering.
Copperplate allows for very fine handwriting.
It will be the standard school handwriting from
the beginning of the 19th century on.

Nach der Renaissance hat die offizielle Schrift einige
Veränderungen erfahren.
 Die Aszendenten (obere Teil des Buchstab
und die Dezendenten
(untere Teil des Buchstabens) verlängern.
Die Schrift verändert sich durch den Einsatz von biegsamer
Metallfedern mit feiner Spitze; die nach und nach die
klassischen Gänsekiele ersetzten.
Die Englische Schreibschrift erlaubt ein flüssiges und feines Sch
Diese Schrift entwickelt sich im 19. Jehrhundert in vielen Lä
Europas zur allgemeinen Schulschrift.

The beauty of this lettering is in the
different thickness of the strokes :
the thick strokes -or blunt- and
the fine strokes -or hairlines.

Die Attraktivität dieser Schrift ist unter ande
der Wechsel der Schriftstärke.

How to get blunt and fine strokes?

Hairlines are made whith an upstroke.
Blunt are made whith a downstroke
lightly spreading the nib.

Wie erreicht man diese unterschiedlichen
Schriftstärken?

Beim Zug der Feder nach oben hast Du ein
feinen Strich, beim Zug nach unten verbre
sich die Feder durch den ausgeübten Druc
Dieses führt zu einem breiten Strich.

A A A A

To learn and practice : a complete alphabet and model lettering.

For each letter, the sequence of the stroke is indicated from left to right. The first stroke is in red (just right of the red block). Next to it, the finished first stroke is in black, and the second stroke is in red. The last black letter is the finished one. This finished letter is also in light blue so you can practice writing over it.

Ein komplettes Alphabet und Beispiele um zu lernen und zu üben.

Jeder Buchstabe ist je nach Strichführung in seine „Bestandteile" zerlegt worden. Der erste Strich ist in rot, rechts daneben findet man diesen ersten Strich in schwarz, der zweite Strich ist wiederum rot usw. Der letzte Buchstabe ist dann das entgültige Muster. Daneben ist noch ein hellblauer Buchstabe, der zum Üben überschrieben werden soll.

A   *A A A A*
    1   2

a   *a a*

B   *L B B B*

b   *b b*

C C C C

c c c

D D D D

d d d

E E E E

e e e

F ʃ T F F F

f f f f

G G G G

g g g g

H H H H H

h h h h

I *I* *I* *I*

i *i* *i* *i*

J *J* *J*

j *j* *j* *j*

K *I* *I* *K* *K* *K*

k *k* *k* *k*

$\mathscr{L}$ $\mathscr{L}$ $\mathscr{L}$

l l l

$\mathscr{M}$ $\mathscr{M}$ $\mathscr{M}$

m m m

$\mathscr{N}$ $\mathscr{N}$ $\mathscr{N}$

n n n

O *O* *O*

o *o*

P *L* *P* *P*

p *p* *p*

Q *Q* *Q*

q *q* *q*

R / *R* *R*

r *r* *r*

S *S* *S*

s *s* *s*

C *C* *C*

t *t* *t* *t*

𝒰 | 𝒰 𝒰 𝒰

𝓊 | 𝓊 𝓊

𝒱 | 𝒱 𝒱 𝒱

𝓋 | 𝓋 𝓋

𝒲 | 𝒲 𝒲 𝒲

𝓌 | 𝓌 𝓌

H   *H*   *H*   *H*   *H*

x   *x*   *x*   *x*

Y   *Y*   *Y*   *Y*

y   *y*   *y*   *y*

Z   *Z*   *Z*   *Z*   *Z*

z   *z*   *z*   *z*

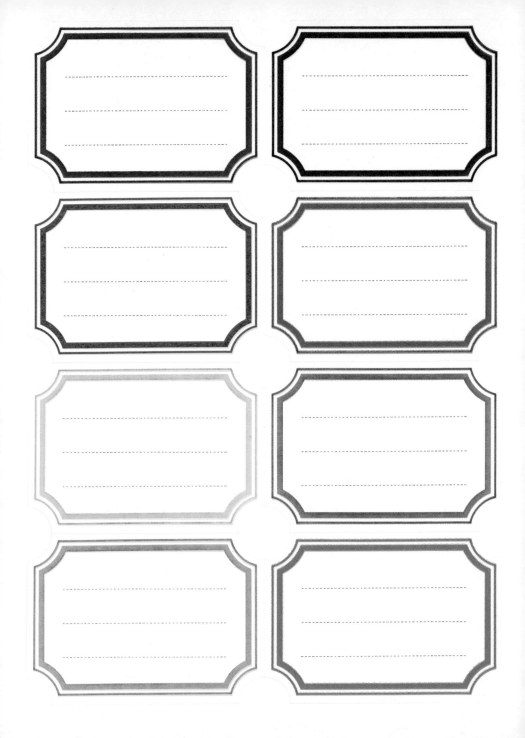

A few examples of Copperplate lettering
Einige Beispiele für die englische Schreibschrift

Assignment book   *Schulheft*

This book belongs to   *Dieses Heft gehört*

Snack -   *Jam*

Halooween   *Merry Christmas -*

Mother - Mama   *Do not disturb - Nicht stören*

Italic lettering
Die runde Schrift

The nibs used for this lettering are "bevel-edged", meaning they are cut at the end at an angle.

We suggest selecting Bandzung (broad-edged) nibs, made in Germany by Brause since 1850.

Die für diese Schrift benötigten Federn sind abgeschrägt.

Wir empfehlen Dir die Bandzugfedern die in Deuschland unverändert seit 1850 hergestellt werden.

Broad-edged/Bandzug

Born during the Renaissance, Italic developed fully during the 18th century growing into a more round and soft writing. Toward the end of the 18th century and the beginning of the 19th, seve variations appeared which would be used into the 20th century especially in registers, accounting books, and other official documents

Ausgehend der schriften der Renaissance kam in der Classic (um 1750) eine runde und weichere Schrift auf.
Im 18.Jahrhundert entwickelten sich viele Varian dieser runden Schrift, die in Registern, Kontenbü und offiziellen Schriftstücken in Europa bis in da 20. Jahrhundert verwendet wurden.

To fully obtain the variations in the stroke thickne the direction, the sequence and the number of strokes must be respected.

Um die verschiedenen Schriftstärken zu erzieler muß man die Richtung des Striches, die Reihenf und die Anzahl der Striche berücksichtigen.

a   *a*

italic/italic   Gothic Italic/Gothik Italic

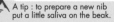

A tip : to prepare a new nib put a little saliva on the beak.

Damit die neue Feder b schreibt, solltest Du ein speichel auf dieSpitze tu

22

To learn and practice : a complete alphabet and model lettering.

For each letter, the sequence of the stroke is indicated from left to right. The first stroke is in red (just right of the red block). Next to it, the finished first stroke is in black, and the second stroke is in red. The last black letter is the finished one. This finished letter is also in light blue so you can practice writing over it.

Ein komplettes Alphabet und Beispiele um zu lernen und zu üben.

Jeder Buchstabe ist je nach Strichführung in seine „Bestandteile" zerlegt wprden. Der erste Strich ist in rot, rechts danben findet man diesen ersten Strich in schwarz, der zweite Strich ist wiederum rot usw. Der letzte Buchstabe ist dann das entgültige Muster. Daneben ist noch ein hellblauer Buchstabe, der zum Üben überschrieben werden soll.

C   *C C C C*

c   *c c c*

D   *D D D D D D*

d   *d d d d*

E   *E E E E*

e   *e e e*

F ʃ ʄ Ƭ Ƒ Ƒ

f ∫ ∫ ∫ ∫

G ℓ G G G

g ℓ ℓ g g g

ℎ l ℎ ℎ ℎ

h l l h h

I *I* *I* *I*

i *i* *i*

J *J* *J* *J* *J* *J*

j *j* *j* *j*

K *L* *L* *K* *K* *k*

k *l* *k* *k* *k*

L $\quad$ L $\quad$ L $\quad$ L $\quad$ L $\quad$ L

l $\quad$ l $\quad$ l $\quad$ l

M $\quad$ S $\quad$ S $\quad$ N $\quad$ M $\quad$ M $\quad$ M

m $\quad$ ı $\quad$ n $\quad$ m $\quad$ m $\quad$ m

N $\quad$ S $\quad$ S $\quad$ N $\quad$ N $\quad$ N

n $\quad$ ı $\quad$ n $\quad$ n $\quad$ n

O 〔 *O* *O* *O*

o 〔 *o* *o* *o*

P 〕 〕 *Y* *P* *P* *P*

p 〕 *p* *p* *p*

Q 〔 *O* *Q* *Q* *Q*

q 〔 *c* *q* *q* *q*

R   ℓ   𝒫   𝒫   ℛ   ℛ

r   ↗   𝓇   𝓇

S   𝒮   𝒮   𝒮

s   ⁄   𝓈   𝓈

T   𝒞   𝒯   𝒯   𝒯

t   𝓉   𝓉   𝓉

U

U U U

u

u u u

V

V V V

v

v v v

W

W W W

w

w w w

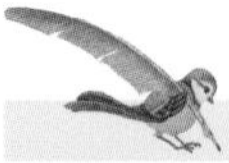

$\mathcal{X}$ $\mathcal{O}$ $\mathcal{X}$ $\mathcal{X}$ $\mathcal{X}$ $\mathcal{X}$

x $\mathcal{o}$ x x x x

$\mathcal{Y}$ $\mathcal{V}$ $\mathcal{V}$ $\mathcal{Y}$ $\mathcal{Y}$ $\mathcal{Y}$

y $\imath$ y y y

$\mathcal{Z}$ γ $\mathcal{J}$ $\mathcal{L}$ $\mathcal{L}$ $\mathcal{L}$

z γ γ $\mathcal{Z}$ $\mathcal{Z}$ z

A few examples of Italic lettering
Einige Beispiele für die runde Schreibschrift

Assignment book   Schulheft

This book belongs to   Dieses Heft gehört

Snack -   Jam

Halooween   Merry Christmas -

Mother - Mama   Do not disturb - Nicht stören